Would You
Rather?

Made You Think!

EDITION

Would You Rather?

Made You Think!

EDITION

Answer Hilarious Questions
& Win the Game of Wits

BY LINDSEY DALY

Z KIDS · NEW YORK

For my parents,
whose unwavering support gives me
the confidence to believe in myself;

for my students past and present,
who have made me a better person;

and for every kid
brave enough to think
outside the box.

Contents

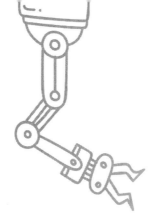

Introduction

The world is full of endless decisions and possibilities. Each and every day, we all make hundreds of little choices. What should I eat for breakfast? What will I wear today? Who will I sit with at lunch? How can I single-handedly overthrow all of the world's leaders and accomplish my dream of total global domination?

Okay, maybe not the last one, but you get the point. In order to successfully make decisions, we must be smart, take time to think things through, and use our creativity to find the best answer. But what makes someone "smart"? Maybe you ace every test after only a small amount of studying. Maybe you build amazing things without using any directions, or you create artistic masterpieces. Perhaps you use humor to entertain people, or you think on your feet and communicate well with others. Everybody is a certified smarty-pants in their own special way.

All it takes to navigate this ever-changing world is a mix of imagination, logic, and outside-the-box thinking.

In today's society, information is being thrown at us constantly. That's why it's important to sharpen those thinking skills and form your own unique opinions and ideas. The most wonderful discovery in life is that there is no "right" answer, and in many instances, it's not *what* you do but *how* you do it. Thinking critically and going on a journey to find *your* answer is where all of the fun happens. It's brave to question, explore, and think creatively. Plus, the best thing you could possibly do for another person is to challenge them to think! This game book provides you with 160 silly, fun, and wacky chances to do just that!

Are you up for the challenge? Grab a few of your friends or family members, and get ready to outthink them! So, how will you solve problems and make your choices? We're about to find out.

Rules of the Game

Get a group of friends or family members together for a game of wits and creativity.
The more the merrier!

* The game is played in 8 levels, with 20 questions in each level. As the levels increase, so does the complexity of the questions.

* Players rotate the responsibility of being the "judge" and reading the question aloud to the group.

* Players will then answer with an explanation and take turns sharing their answers.

* The judge of that round will choose the best answer—it could be the smartest, the funniest, or the most creative. Write the winner's name in the space provided below the question and assign

them 1 point. If only two people are playing, the judge (the player reading the question) assigns 1 to 5 points for the answer (5 being the best answer) and records it with the other player's name in the space provided below the question.

* When all players complete the level, tally up the points to determine the winner for that level.

* In the event of a tie at the end of a level, the two players who are tied will answer the "tiebreaker" question. All remaining players will vote on the best answer. If only two people are playing, whoever makes the other player laugh wins.

When players complete the book, the winner of the most levels is the champion!

LEVEL

1

Smart Starts

Would you rather

kiss a fish that's been living
in a radioactive pond

or

roll down a hill while hugging
a porcupine?

WINNER: POINTS:

Would you rather

have one best friend

or

five friends who don't
know you really well?

WINNER: POINTS:

Would you rather
take a private tour of
a space shuttle
or
a submarine?

WINNER: POINTS:

Would you rather
get a summer job at
an alpaca farm
or
herding sheep?

WINNER: POINTS:

Would you rather

get stranded on an island

or

lost in the middle of the woods?

WINNER: POINTS:

Would you rather

ride through the forest

on a unicorn

or

spend a day hanging out

with Bigfoot?

WINNER: POINTS:

Would you rather
have cotton candy for hair
or
spaghetti?

WINNER: POINTS:

Would you rather
have a pet platypus
or
a pet aardvark?

WINNER: POINTS:

Would you rather
work as a
rodeo clown
or
as a lion tamer
at the circus?

WINNER: POINTS:

Would you rather
play a game one-on-one with
your favorite athlete
or
sing a duet with your
favorite singer?

WINNER: POINTS:

Would you rather

drink dirty dishwater from the sink

or

someone else's bathwater?

WINNER: POINTS:

Would you rather

discover an alien
in your backyard

or

a new animal species?

WINNER: POINTS:

Would you rather

have control over
when it rains

or

when it snows?

WINNER: POINTS:

Would you rather

get spit on by a llama

or

pooped on by a cow?

WINNER: POINTS:

Would you rather

spend a year walking on
stilts every day

or

jumping from place to place
on a pogo stick?

WINNER: POINTS:

Would you rather

use a stranger's toothbrush
to brush your teeth

or

another person's used tissue
to blow your nose?

WINNER: POINTS:

Would you rather

wake up one morning
as a mermaid

or

a centaur?

WINNER: POINTS:

Would you rather

spend a year living in an
igloo in the Arctic

or

living in a tree house
in the Amazon rain forest?

WINNER: POINTS:

Would you rather
have the ability to be invisible
whenever you choose
or
the power to make other people
disappear at your command?

WINNER: POINTS:

Would you rather
spend the rest of your life
without television
or

video games?

WINNER: POINTS:

Would you rather
be a passenger on the first
commercial flight to Mars
or
a passenger on the
first public bus tour
of Area 51?

WINNER: POINTS:

WINNER:
_____

TOTAL POINTS:
_____

LEVEL

2

Playful
Picks

Would you rather
throw up in front of
your whole class
or
fart in front of your teacher?

WINNER: POINTS:

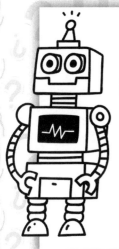

Would you rather
have a robot that does
all of your chores
or
completes your
school projects?

WINNER: POINTS:

Would you rather

explore the inside of
an ancient pyramid

or

the inside of a cave that contains
prehistoric paintings?

WINNER: POINTS:

Would you rather

lose your sense of smell

or

taste?

WINNER: POINTS:

Would you rather
have a pet sloth
or
a pet koala?

WINNER: POINTS:

Would you rather
grow a horsetail
or
have scaly skin like a fish?

WINNER: POINTS:

Would you rather
be the host of your own talk show

or

the star of a Broadway show?

WINNER: POINTS:

Would you rather
find out that your best friend
is an alien from another planet

or

a werewolf?

WINNER: POINTS:

Would you rather

ride on the back of a killer whale

or

a saber-toothed tiger?

WINNER: POINTS:

Would you rather

win a lifetime supply of clothes
from one store

or

$500 to spend in
any store you wanted?

WINNER: POINTS:

Would you rather
be an Olympic bobsledder
or
a sword-swallower?

WINNER: POINTS:

Would you rather
find a fingernail in your soup
or
a used Band-Aid in your
mashed potatoes?

WINNER: POINTS:

Would you rather

have an inflatable bouncy house
in your bedroom

or

a slide that leads to the outside?

WINNER: POINTS:

Would you rather

be stuck in the middle
of the ocean in a rowboat

or

in the desert on
a skateboard?

WINNER: POINTS:

Would you rather
sleep with a blanket made
out of sandpaper
or
tree bark?

WINNER: POINTS:

Would you rather
have a seashell for a nose
or
a pine cone?

WINNER: POINTS:

Would you rather
give an alligator a bath
or
swim in a pool with a shark?

WINNER: POINTS:

Would you rather
eat tuna fish–flavored ice cream
or
drink a garlic-flavored milkshake?

WINNER: POINTS:

Would you rather
hop from place to place
like a frog

or

slither around
like a snake?

WINNER: POINTS:

Would you rather
walk a mile on a slippery sheet of ice

or

through thick mud?

WINNER: POINTS:

Would you rather
have a photographic
memory
or
psychic abilities?

WINNER: POINTS:

WINNER:
_____

TOTAL POINTS:
_____

LEVEL

3

Savvy Selections

Would you rather

carry a 10-pound bowling ball
with you everywhere
you went for a week

or

a large cactus?

WINNER: POINTS:

Would you rather

spend a day completely
submerged in butter

or

covered in superglue?

WINNER: POINTS:

Would you rather
have a multilevel tree house
with electricity in your backyard

or

an in-ground pool
with a waterslide?

WINNER: POINTS:

Would you rather
have four legs

or

a second pair of eyes
in the back of your head?

WINNER: POINTS:

Would you rather
eat birthday cake
with brussels sprout filling
or
mustard-flavored icing?

WINNER: POINTS:

Would you rather
receive a brand-new car on
the day you get your driver's license
or
a check for $10,000?

WINNER: POINTS:

Would you rather

work as a stunt person

or

as a bodyguard for a celebrity?

WINNER: POINTS:

Would you rather

have movie star parents

or

a sibling who's a
professional athlete?

WINNER: POINTS:

Would you rather

wake up in a parallel universe
where talking dogs are
in charge of the planet

or

where robots are the
world's leaders?

WINNER: POINTS:

Would you rather

spend a day wearing wet jeans

or

shoes that are two sizes too small?

WINNER: POINTS:

Would you rather
brush your teeth with
pickle-flavored toothpaste

or

wash your body with
onion-scented soap?

WINNER: POINTS:

Would you rather
win a lifetime supply of
your favorite candy

or

movie tickets?

WINNER: POINTS:

Would you rather
live in a house with 30 pet cats
or
15 pet guinea pigs?

WINNER: POINTS:

Would you rather
walk around the mall in a
full suit of armor
or
a gymnastics leotard?

WINNER: POINTS:

Would you rather
have your face added to
Mount Rushmore
or
receive a star on the
Hollywood Walk of Fame?

WINNER: POINTS:

Would you rather
chew on a piece of tinfoil
or
have sand stuck in your teeth?

WINNER: POINTS:

Would you rather
have your laugh replaced
by the sound of an air horn
or
a wailing siren?

WINNER: POINTS:

Would you rather
fall on a fragile school project
you just spent two hours making
or
drop a birthday cake you baked for
a family member in the dirt?

WINNER: POINTS:

Would you rather

drink a gallon of milk minutes
before sprinting in a track meet

or

eat an entire pizza just before
riding a roller coaster?

WINNER: POINTS:

Would you rather

interview a soldier from the
American Revolutionary War

or

a knight from the Middle Ages?

WINNER: POINTS:

Would you rather

be stuck at the top
of a Ferris wheel

or

in a graveyard at night?

WINNER: POINTS:

WINNER:
_____

TOTAL POINTS:
_____

LEVEL

4

Challenging Choices

Would you rather
spend a night trapped
in an amusement park
or
a zoo?

WINNER: POINTS:

Would you rather
be the size of an ant
for an entire week
or
the size of a giraffe?

WINNER: POINTS:

Would you rather

be face-to-face with Dracula

or

the Loch Ness
Monster?

WINNER: POINTS:

Would you rather

find a backpack full of diamonds

or

an old trunk filled with gold?

WINNER: POINTS:

Would you rather
fly in a hot-air balloon
over the countryside
or
ride in a helicopter over
a famous city?

WINNER: POINTS:

Would you rather
drive the world's fastest car
or
be a passenger on
the world's
fastest airplane?

WINNER: POINTS:

Would you rather
get sprayed with a hose
on a freezing cold day
or
sit in a hot tub on a
sizzling summer day?

WINNER: POINTS:

Would you rather
eat a bagel
covered in earwax
or
boogers?

WINNER: POINTS:

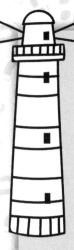

Would you rather
work as a lighthouse keeper
or
a railroad conductor?

WINNER: POINTS:

Would you rather
study pandas in their natural habitat
or
observe the migration patterns of penguins?

WINNER: POINTS:

Would you rather
be the world's best chess master
or
Ping-Pong player?

WINNER: POINTS:

Would you rather
eat a jar of mayonnaise
or
drink a bottle of cooking oil?

WINNER: POINTS:

Would you rather
be able to shoot lightning
out of your fingertips
or
create hurricane-force
winds with your mind?

WINNER: POINTS:

Would you rather
eat a live snail
or
a dead bumblebee?

WINNER: POINTS:

Would you rather

have peacock feathers

or

tiger-striped skin?

WINNER: POINTS:

Would you rather

have to rescue a hostage from
an underground dungeon
protected by guards

or

from a pirate ship?

WINNER: POINTS:

Would you rather

live on a cruise ship that
always travels to new destinations

or

in a beachfront mansion?

WINNER: POINTS:

Would you rather

work as an
undercover CIA agent

or

as a nuclear
engineer?

WINNER: POINTS:

Would you rather
take a ride on a magic carpet
or
on a flying broomstick?

WINNER: POINTS:

Would you rather
sprain your ankle the day before a
championship basketball game
or
lose your voice the night of
the school musical?

WINNER: POINTS:

Would you rather

hike to the top of a volcano

or

take a tour of an old gold mine?

WINNER: POINTS:

WINNER:
_____

TOTAL POINTS:
_____

LEVEL

5

Difficult
Decisions

Would you rather
accidentally kill your friend's
plants that they've been
growing for years
or
their pet goldfish?

WINNER: POINTS:

Would you rather
go paintballing
with your school principal
or
play laser tag against
all of your teachers?

WINNER: POINTS:

Would you rather

salsa dance with a ninja

or

a zombie?

WINNER: POINTS:

Would you rather

be a character in a movie

or

in a book?

WINNER: POINTS:

Would you rather
give up eating in restaurants
for the rest of your life
or
going to see movies
in movie theaters?

WINNER: POINTS:

Would you rather
win an award in school
for being the kindest student
or
the smartest?

WINNER: POINTS:

Would you rather

win a trip to an amusement park but get the flu the day you arrive

or

win a trip to a tropical island where it rains every day?

WINNER: POINTS:

Would you rather

take a bath in a tub full of macaroni and cheese

or

a shower under a stream of barbecue sauce?

WINNER: POINTS:

Would you rather

run 10 miles with an ingrown toenail

or

walk barefoot for 20 miles
on gravel roads?

WINNER: POINTS:

Would you rather

sing in front of
10 of your classmates

or

perform a choreographed
dance routine in front of
50 strangers?

WINNER: POINTS:

Would you rather
ride down the world's
tallest waterslide
or
jump on the world's
largest trampoline?

WINNER: POINTS:

Would you rather
meet your favorite celebrity
and find out they're mean
or
never have a chance to
meet them at all?

WINNER: POINTS:

Would you rather
play a game of soccer
while wearing flip-flops
or
a game of baseball using
an oven mitt instead
of a baseball glove?

WINNER: POINTS:

Would you rather
be the shortest
person in the world
or
the tallest?

WINNER: POINTS:

Would you rather

have a tutor who does
your homework

or

a personal chef who prepares
any food you want?

WINNER: POINTS:

Would you rather

live in the apartment below
professional yodelers

or

the drummer for
a heavy metal band?

WINNER: POINTS:

Would you rather

become best friends with the son
or daughter of a famous celebrity

or

be the child of the president
of the United States?

WINNER: POINTS:

Would you rather

spend a week trapped inside
the body of a dolphin that lives
in an aquarium

or

a tropical fish that
lives in its natural habitat?

WINNER: POINTS:

Would you rather

have a glob of grape jelly fly out of
your throat every time you cough

or

ketchup come out of your nose
whenever you sneeze?

Would you rather

be able to understand any language

or

know how to play any instrument?

TIEBREAKER

Would you rather

have your personal diary read
aloud to the whole school once

or

have an embarrassing
video of you posted on YouTube
for a year?

WINNER: POINTS:

WINNER:
_____

TOTAL POINTS:
_____

LEVEL

6

Clever
Contests

Would you rather

spend the day living
inside the setting
of your favorite book

or

your favorite video game?

WINNER: POINTS:

Would you rather

go outside to find it
raining hot sauce

or

ranch dressing?

WINNER: POINTS:

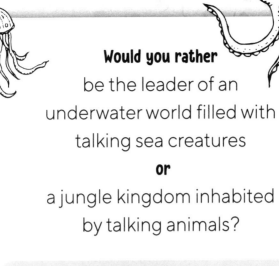

Would you rather
be the leader of an
underwater world filled with
talking sea creatures

or

a jungle kingdom inhabited
by talking animals?

WINNER: POINTS:

Would you rather
get every question wrong
on a game show

or

forget all the words to
your song on a singing show?

WINNER: POINTS:

Would you rather

have music come on every time
you walked into a room

or

an automatic laugh track play
every time you made a joke?

WINNER: POINTS:

Would you rather

have a nightmare once a week

or

a fairly bad dream
every night of the week?

WINNER: POINTS:

Would you rather

eat a cake that was made using salt instead of sugar

or

a batch of cookies made with chunks of fish in place of chocolate chips?

WINNER: POINTS:

Would you rather

open your backpack to find a rotten banana

or

expired bologna?

WINNER: POINTS:

Would you rather

live a double life as a superhero who
secretly saves hundreds of people

or

save one person and be
praised as a local hero?

WINNER: POINTS:

Would you rather

travel back in time to find out what
really happened to Amelia Earhart

or

discover the truth about how
Stonehenge was built?

WINNER: POINTS:

Would you rather

share a sleeping bag
with a nonvenomous snake

or

sleep in a small room
with an angry wasp?

WINNER: POINTS:

Would you rather

get stuck in an elevator
for 24 hours with a smelly person

or

be stuck in a dark cave
for 24 hours by yourself?

WINNER: POINTS:

Would you rather
time travel to a day 100 years ago
or
a day 100 years in the future?

WINNER: POINTS:

Would you rather
live in a house made
entirely out of cheese
or
crackers?

WINNER: POINTS:

Would you rather

have a national holiday
created in your honor

or

a large monument built for you?

WINNER: POINTS:

Would you rather

live on the top floor
of a skyscraper in a big city

or

in a beachfront hut on an island?

WINNER: POINTS:

Would you rather

be forced to wear a fake witch nose
on school picture day
or
a clown wig?

WINNER: POINTS:

Would you rather

be celebrated for an achievement
that wasn't yours
or
watch another person take credit for
something you accomplished?

WINNER: POINTS:

Would you rather

go to a school that holds
all of its classes outside

or

takes its students on a field trip
once every month?

WINNER: POINTS:

Would you rather

get locked in a porta-potty overnight

or

a school locker?

WINNER: POINTS:

Would you rather
eat a fried toad
or
a fried raccoon?

WINNER: POINTS:

WINNER: _____

TOTAL POINTS: _____

LEVEL

7

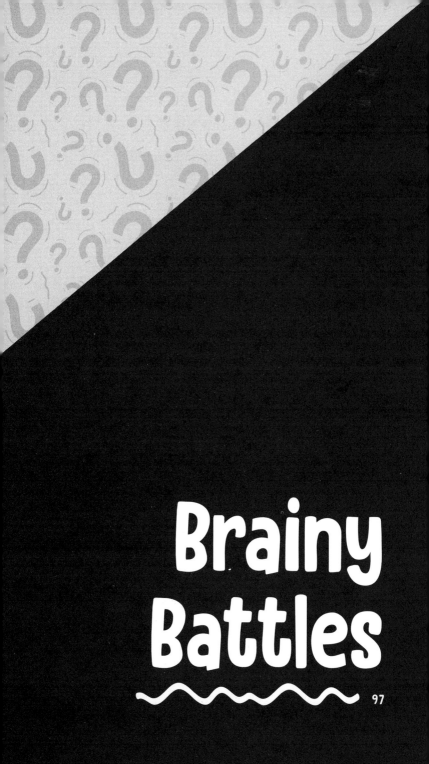

Brainy Battles

Would you rather
have a self-driving car
or
a car that can fly?

WINNER: POINTS:

Would you rather
bike two
miles uphill
or
swim one mile against
the current?

WINNER: POINTS:

Would you rather
your bedroom smell like
the inside of a sweaty
gym sneaker

or

raw sewage?

WINNER: POINTS:

Would you rather
be able to walk on water

or

through fire?

WINNER: POINTS:

Would you rather

complete an obstacle course
in high heels

or

a swimming race
in a puffy winter coat?

WINNER: POINTS:

Would you rather

put your retainer back
in your mouth after it fell into
the cafeteria garbage can

or

eat a sandwich out of a dumpster?

WINNER: POINTS:

Would you rather
have a turtle shell
or
crab claws?

WINNER: POINTS:

Would you rather
referee the Super Bowl
or
be a judge at the
Olympic Games?

WINNER: POINTS:

Would you rather

have access to a library that contains
a copy of every book ever written

or

a museum that houses every dinosaur
bone that's ever been discovered?

WINNER: POINTS:

Would you rather

have a neighbor who cuts
down trees with a chain saw
every night at 11:00 p.m.

or

shoots off fireworks
every morning at 6:00 a.m.?

WINNER: POINTS:

Would you rather

eat your dog's vomit
every day for a week

or

swallow a live spider
every day for a month?

WINNER: POINTS:

Would you rather

have a $10 bill that regenerates
every time you spend it

or

an unlimited amount of pennies?

WINNER: POINTS:

Would you rather

have hands in place of your feet

or

feet in place of your hands?

WINNER: POINTS:

Would you rather

lose the money that was going
to pay for a big school field trip

or

lose clothing donations that your
classmates collected for kids in need?

WINNER: POINTS:

Would you rather
bungee jump off a tall building
in a bustling city
or
off a bridge over a large river?

WINNER: POINTS:

Would you rather
trade lives for a day
with a professional wrestler
or
a news reporter?

WINNER: POINTS:

Would you rather

have your favorite author
answer all of your questions

or

read a copy of the sequel
to your favorite book
before anyone else?

WINNER: POINTS:

Would you rather

get sprayed by a
skunk moments before
attending an
important event

or

peed on by a horse?

WINNER: POINTS:

Would you rather

lead an organization that
brings an end to animal cruelty

or

that reverses the effects
of air pollution?

WINNER: POINTS:

Would you rather

grow a giant horn from
the center of your forehead

or

a pair of tiny, nonfunctional wings?

WINNER: POINTS:

Would you rather

get caught in a powerful
rainstorm without an umbrella

or

in a blizzard without a coat?

WINNER: POINTS:

WINNER:

_____

TOTAL POINTS:

_____

LEVEL

8

Master's Match

Would you rather
spend the night alone
in your house after
watching a horror film
or
in a haunted house with
one other person?

WINNER: POINTS:

Would you rather
constantly have dry, itchy skin
or
clammy, sweaty hands?

WINNER: POINTS:

Would you rather
have everything you eat
taste like rotten eggs
or
everything you drink
taste like spoiled milk?

WINNER: POINTS:

Would you rather
go a year without
taking a shower
or
6 months without brushing
your teeth?

WINNER: POINTS:

Would you rather

find a stranger's hair in your meal
after you've eaten most of it

or

a dead insect in the dessert
you almost finished?

WINNER: POINTS:

Would you rather

have the ability to
communicate with animals

or

choose 10 people's minds to
read anytime you want?

WINNER: POINTS:

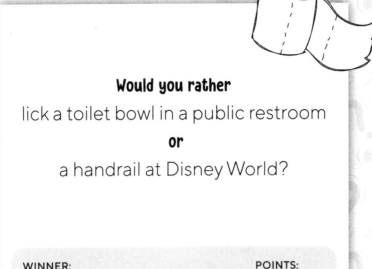

Would you rather

lick a toilet bowl in a public restroom

or

a handrail at Disney World?

WINNER: POINTS:

Would you rather

pop a stranger's pimple

or

rub cream on their rash?

WINNER: POINTS:

Would you rather
play the lottery and win
one lump sum of $500,000
or
win $1,000 a week for
the next 20 years?

WINNER: POINTS:

Would you rather
wake up at a sleepover
to discover your friends cut your
hair into a Mohawk
or
shaved off both of your eyebrows?

WINNER: POINTS:

Would you rather

drink a cow's milk
directly from its udders

or

take a bite of
honey straight from
a beehive?

WINNER: POINTS:

Would you rather

hear a loud ringing sound in your
ears for the rest of your life

or

have an itch that never goes away
even when you scratch it?

WINNER: POINTS:

Would you rather
be able to communicate
with the dead
or
with other people
telepathically?

WINNER: POINTS:

Would you rather
lick a dusty bookshelf
or
take a bite out of a
chunk of mold?

WINNER: POINTS:

Would you rather
have the ability to teleport
or
to fly?

WINNER: POINTS:

Would you rather
know all of history
or
have the ability to
predict the future?

WINNER: POINTS:

Would you rather
lick a slimy slug
or
have a camel lick the inside
of your mouth?

WINNER: POINTS:

Would you rather
let your fingernails
grow 11 inches long
or
go 6 months without
washing your feet?

WINNER: POINTS:

Would you rather
drink a magical potion
that gives you
superhuman strength
or
speed?

WINNER: POINTS:

Would you rather
eat a doughnut with
insect guts as frosting
or
a slice of pizza topped
with snakeskin?

WINNER: POINTS:

Would you rather
be an expert archer
or
a professional fencer?

WINNER: POINTS:

WINNER:
_____

TOTAL POINTS:
_____

This certificate
is awarded to

_____

for being a legend of logic,
a heavyweight of humor,
and a captain of creativity!

Tough choices are
no match for you.

CONGRATULATIONS!

About the Author

 **Lindsey Daly** grew up in Andover, New Jersey. She graduated from Ramapo College of New Jersey with a BA in History and a certification in Secondary Education. When she is not writing, Lindsey is working as a middle school social studies teacher and managing an Instagram page targeted at educators. She lives with her dog, Teddy, in New Jersey.

Instagram: **@lindseydalybooks**
Twitter: **@LindseyDaly10**